W9-AWF-965

מסורה

ArtScroll® Youth Series

Rabbi Nosson Scherman / Rabbi Gedaliah Zlotowitz
General Editors
Rabbi Meir Zlotowitz ז״ל, *Founder*

Published by

ARTSCROLL

Mesorah Publications, ltd

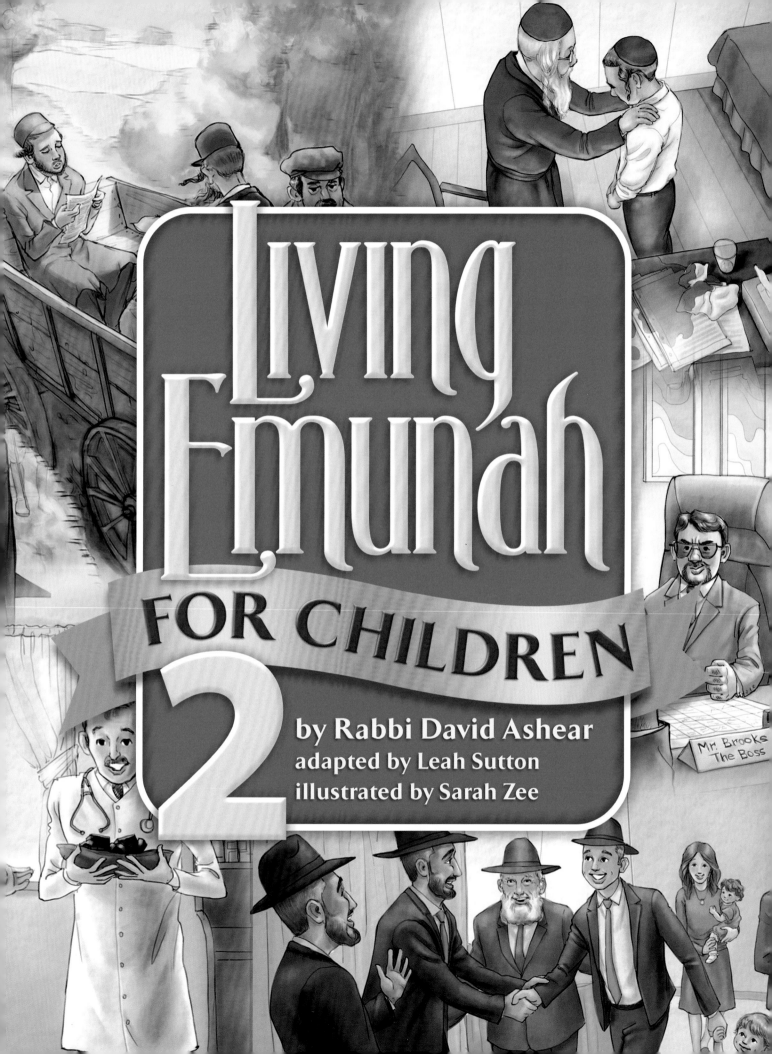

Living Emunah

FOR CHILDREN

2

by Rabbi David Ashear
adapted by Leah Sutton
illustrated by Sarah Zee

RTSCROLL® YOUTH SERIES

"LIVING EMUNAH FOR CHILDREN 2"

Published by **MESORAH PUBLICATIONS, LTD.**
4401 Second Avenue / Brooklyn, N.Y 11232 / (718) 921-9000 / Fax: (718) 680-1875
www.artscroll.com

Illustrated by Sarah Zee.

Distributed in Israel by **SIFRIATI / A. GITLER**
POB 2351 / Bnei Brak 51122 / Israel / 03-579-8187

Distributed in Europe by **LEHMANNS**
Unit E, Viking Business Park, Rolling Mill Road / Jarrow, Tyne and Wear / England NE32 3DP

Distributed in Australia and New Zealand by **GOLDS WORLD OF JUDAICA**
3-13 William Street / Balaclava, Melbourne 3183 / Victoria, Australia

Distributed in South Africa by **KOLLEL BOOKSHOP**
Northfield Centre / 17 Northfield Avenue / Glenhazel 2192 / Johannesburg, South Africa

Printed in the United States of America by Noble Book Press Corp.
Custom bound by Sefercraft, Inc. / 4401 Second Avenue / Brooklyn N.Y. 11232

ISBN-10: 1-4226-2315-7
ISBN-13: 978-1-4226-2315-2

I would like to thank **Hashem** for guiding this project throughout.

A special thanks to the people who worked hard to bring it to reality: **Rabbi David Sutton** for coordinating this project; **Leah Sutton** for choosing and adapting the stories from *Living Emunah*; **Rabbi Nosson Scherman** and **Mrs. Goldie Golding** for their editorial input; **Sarah Zee** for her delightful illustrations that make the stories come alive; **Chana Sternglantz** for the beautiful page layout and **Eli Kroen** for the magnificent cover design; **Mendy Herzberg** and the entire **ArtScroll team;** lastly, the generous sponsors. Thank you to my dear in-laws, **Barbara** and **Bob Matalon,** for graciously dedicating this book. May Hashem bless you with the strength to continue all of your hard work on behalf of our community. May this book be accepted by the public and inspire children to a life of Emunah.

Rabbi David Ashear

Table of Contents

The Best Bris

"Rabbi, Rabbi!"

Rabbi Yehuda Tzadka turned around to see someone he didn't recognize calling his name.

"My wife gave birth to a baby boy last Shabbos! Would you agree to be the *mohel* for my son's *bris* this Shabbos?"

"*Mazel tov!*" he replied.

Although Rabbi Yehuda Tzadka was old, and it was a long walk to the man's home on Shabbos, he agreed. And so, that Shabbos, Rabbi Tzadka walked together with his attendant, Moshe, to perform the *bris*.

They got to the house just in time, but for some reason, the *bris* was not starting yet. Within a few minutes, the reason for the delay became clear. The father had changed his mind and invited another *mohel* to do the *bris*.

"I am embarrassed to say this," he tried to explain, "but —"

"Not a problem!" R' Tzadka said calmly. "Just do the mitzvah as quickly as possible."

Again, they waited, but the *bris* still wasn't starting.

"Rabbi Tzadka," the father apologized, "it seems that the other *mohel* forgot to bring his supplies. Can we use yours?"

"Of course, of course," the rav answered, with a warm smile.

The other *mohel* performed the *bris*, and R' Tzadka headed back home together with his attendant.

"I cannot believe what happened," Moshe said, amazed. "We came from so far to do this *bris*! Not only did he get a different *mohel* to do

it, but he had the *chutzpah* to ask you for your equipment! How were you able to remain so calm and kind to the man?"

"Moshe," R' Tzadka explained, "I've done thousands of *brisos* in my lifetime. Today, however, I had a very precious opportunity." His eyes sparkled and he explained.

"*Chazal* teach us that if someone *tries* to do a mitzvah but is not able to, Hashem considers it as if he did that mitzvah." He paused.

"Whenever I perform a *bris*, everyone there honors me. Therefore, I am not sure I can say that I did the mitzvah for the right reasons. But today, I tried to do the *bris*, so it is like I did the mitzvah, but I didn't get any honor." He turned to face Moshe. "Now do you see why I am so happy? This is the best *bris* I could have had!"

Rabbi Tzadka knew everything that happens is from Hashem. He did not get upset or insulted — he was even happy!

We must try to always believe that no one can take away anything from us unless Hashem wants them to have it. This way, we will never get angry at anyone; we will know that everything comes from Hashem and we will be able to feel real happiness for our friends.

Royal Treatment

Some people think of Hashem as a strict judge Who waits to punish them as soon as they do something wrong. But that is not true! Hashem loves all of us more than we can imagine.

The Gemara tells us that if someone wanted to take something out of his pocket, but by mistake he took out the wrong thing, Hashem considers that as if the person just suffered!

Hashem loves us so much that it pains Him for even such a small thing to happen to us.

One day, Rav Shmuel's wife heard a knock at their door. A heavy man with a curly mustache was standing there. He gave her a parchment and left.

She looked at the parchment, puzzled. With a jump, she noticed the queen's seal stamped on the outside. She hurried to Rav Shmuel. With trembling hands, she handed him the parchment. Rav Shmuel calmly opened the letter.

> Honored Rabbi,
> The queen requests an audience with the Rabbi at her palace tomorrow. She is greatly looking forward to your presence.

Rav Shmuel went right back to his Torah learning.

The next day, a royal carriage pulled up to Rav Shmuel's house. He did not notice the pure gold handles, fine silk curtains, and plush purple seats. Rav Shmuel was thinking about the Torah he had been learning.

Soon, they arrived at the palace. The queen was sitting on her throne, wearing her royal gown. On her lap was her newborn son. Rav Shmuel watched quietly as the queen held him up.

"Rabbi, how I love this child! My days have become so much more enjoyable with him now. For the rest of my life, all that I shall do is make sure he's comfortable. He will never, ever, suffer. I will make sure of that, Rabbi!"

"Your Highness," Rav Shmuel asked, "what happens if your son wishes to get a tissue from his pocket, but instead of putting his hand in the right pocket where the tissue is, he puts it in the left one first? Or, say, he wishes to eat an apple, but mistakenly reaches for an orange instead. How will you make sure he doesn't go through this kind of suffering?"

"Oh," she answered, "that's not suffering. It wouldn't bother me!"

Rav Shmuel congratulated the queen and left the palace. He looked up and said, "This queen loves her only child so much, but it wouldn't bother her if he put his hand in the wrong pocket. But You, Hashem, You love Your children so much, that even **that** You consider suffering!"

We are all Hashem's children. He wants only the best for us all!

Seeing Miracles

E zra adjusted his *tefillin* and glanced in his mirror to make sure it was in the right place on his head. Something was wrong with his mirror. He rubbed the mirror clean and squinted; he brought it closer to his eyes. No, it wasn't the mirror, Ezra realized. It was his *eyes*. He could barely see.

Right after *davening*, Ezra rushed to his eye doctor's office.

"It doesn't look good, Ezra," the doctor said with a frown. "I want you to go to a specialist to have this checked."

Later that afternoon, Ezra found himself in the office of a top eye doctor.

"I am afraid you are losing your eyesight," the specialist told him in a deep voice. "I want you to go to the best doctor in America." He gave Ezra the telephone number. "Make an appointment and see what he can do."

Two days later, Ezra was at the doctor's office. As he waited, he dropped his head and tears fell. *Oh, Hashem, only three nights ago I went to sleep able to see everything, and now I may not see anything ever again! Please help me!* he cried.

The doctor spent a while examining Ezra's eyes. "You are in great danger of losing your eyesight," he explained. "I will need to do a difficult and dangerous operation right away to try and help you."

"Can it wait a bit?" Ezra asked. "I'll come back later today."

The doctor agreed, and Ezra walked along the streets searching for a shul. He found one; it was empty. He wanted to beg Hashem to let him continue to see the precious things around him. He thought about what Hashem had given him to enjoy until now, and he began to thank Hashem.

"Thank You, Hashem, for my devoted wife ... for my beautiful children and grandchildren ... for my ears and my mind, for the Torah ...."

He also gave thanks for the small things.

"Thank You, Hashem, for getting me a good seat on the plane, for helping me find a shul quickly ...." Only after Ezra finished thanking Hashem for everything did he ask Hashem to let him continue seeing. When he checked the time, three hours had passed. He hurried back to the doctor and waited for the operation to begin.

Right before the surgery, the doctor noticed something different about Ezra's eyes.

"I apologize for frightening you, Ezra. It appears you are going to be okay. I can't believe I missed that detail before, but you don't need the surgery."

Upon hearing these words, Ezra smiled and thanked Hashem once more.

Saying "Thank You" to Hashem is so powerful and precious to Him. When Hashem sees that we appreciate all He does, He wants to give us even more.

A Big Gift

"It's a boy!"

Sounds of happiness could be heard from Talya's room on the third floor of the hospital. This was the third son to be born to Talya and Ron Meiri, a non-religious couple living in Israel.

The nurses finished weighing and checking the baby, and then handed him to Talya. She smiled weakly while gently stroking her newborn son's head. But then Talya saw something that made her stop mid-stroke.

"Ron!" She called to her husband urgently.

Ron turned toward her quickly.

"Ron, look at his ears!" she cried in a whisper. "Oh, just *look* at them!"

Ron stared at his newborn son's ears. They were, well, rather large, if not gigantic.

He tried to hide his feelings from his wife. "He's beautiful, Talya. Just perfect," he said quickly.

But Talya didn't hear him. "No, Ron. No. I see you just don't understand. I can *never let anyone* see these ears!"

Ron tried to quiet her, but true to her word, Talya kept baby Eli hidden from most people. Only close friends and family saw him from time to time.

Soon enough, it was time for Eli to start going to school. Talya was at a loss. Where should she send him? She couldn't keep him home any longer!

One of Talya's best friends had a suggestion. "Why don't you send him to one of those religious schools where the boys all walk around

with those long *peyos* that cover their ears? If his ears are covered with *peyos*, no one will see them!"

Talya never would send her son to a religious school! Her two older sons were in non-religious schools.

"Let's do it," she told her husband over dinner that night. "I am too embarrassed to have people see his ears."

And so, Eli Meiri began to attend nursery in what would become fourteen years in a true Torah yeshivah. He then went on to *beis medrash* and *kollel*, and from there, built a beautiful, religious family.

One night, while Talya and Ron were sipping hot mint tea on their porch, Talya said, "Having Eli was so difficult for me. I was so embarrassed of his ears, but look now! I am so proud of Eli, and of the righteous *ben Torah* he has become."

Big ears seemed so terrible at first. But now, much later, we are able to see how it was really for the best.

"This is also for the good!" We must say it and believe it. Everything Hashem does is for our best.

A Couple of Cups

Mike wiped his forehead. He looked at the list of how much money he had earned that year. He frowned. "I must think of a plan to earn more," he said, as he tapped his fingers against his desk.

Mike sold packages of plastic cups to stores. One night, while tossing in his bed, Mike came up with a plan. *If I put only 99 cups in each package instead of 100, I will save a lot of money! On the package, it'll still say that it has 100 cups inside. No one will know.*

During the next few months, Mike made more money than usual. *Hmm. Why don't I leave out another cup?* he thought.

Soon, Mike was putting in only 97 cups. Slowly, 97 made its way down to 95 and even 92.

One weekend, Mike was at a hotel. He didn't know that there was also a program there to help people come closer to Hashem and His Torah. After breakfast, Mike decided to check it out. He sat through one speech, and then another. Mike was so amazed! He went over to one of the rabbis during a break.

The rabbi introduced himself as Rabbi Marcus. They spoke, and soon after, Mike began learning with Rabbi Marcus each night over the phone. He learned what it means to be Jewish, and to make a *Kiddush Hashem*. Mike felt terrible for what he was doing with the cups. He decided to ask Rav Elyashiv what to do.

"Reb Michael," Rav Elyashiv instructed him, "from now on, you should put 108 cups in each package — to make up for the eight that were missing."

Mike knew that he would lose money that way. Nevertheless, he followed Rav Elyashiv's directions.

Mike began to make less money but still kept putting 108 cups in every package.

One day, a worker came to Mike's office with a newspaper. Someone wrote an article about companies that cheat people by giving fewer items than what the package says. The article wrote about an honest company — Mike's — that put eight extra cups in its packages. They encouraged people to buy cups from Mike.

Soon, many more stores wanted to sell his cups. Mike decided to sell forks, knives, spoons, plates, and napkins. In no time at all, Mike was making a lot of money!

But the best part was that Mike had made a Kiddush Hashem. Even if it seems that no one notices, Hashem sees everything! He will pay everyone back for the good deeds they've done.

The Elegance of Humility

Shimon was an excellent tailor. All the rich people came to him to sew suits for them. One day, the prince himself ordered a suit from Shimon.

Shimon carefully measured the prince, then went to his shop and began to work. He hummed proudly to himself as his machine hummed along. *Yes, for the prince only the best will do. That surely is why he came to me,* his heart sang joyously.

"Sorry," he told everyone who entered his shop. "I am extremely busy sewing a suit for the prince. Please come back in a few weeks."

Finally, the suit was ready. With a big smile, he proudly showed it to the prince. But before Shimon could even say a word, the prince threw the suit on the floor.

"You call yourself an expert tailor?!" he screamed furiously. "Who taught you how to sew? This suit is a disgrace!"

Shimon was brokenhearted. With tears of shame, he ran to his Rav and told him what had happened.

"Rebbi," he cried out, "I'm finished! I'm worthless! No one will order anything from me ever again. I thought I was a good tailor, and now I see I'm worth less than nothing!"

"Shimon," the Rav advised, "go home and take out all the stitches you made in the suit. Then sew it back together exactly like before. When you are done, bring it back to the prince."

Two weeks later, Shimon returned to his Rav. "Tell me, Rebbi, what miracle did you perform? I did exactly what you said and brought the suit back to the prince. The minute I showed it to him, he smiled and said that it was the most beautiful suit he had ever seen. He paid me more than I could've ever dreamed. He even ordered more suits! But

Rebbi, you and I know that it was the same suit. Why did he like it more the second time?"

The Rav explained, "When you sewed the suit the first time, you were proud of yourself and full of *gaavah*. When you did it the second time, you felt humble and broken. The *pasuk* in *Mishlei* says, *V'la'anavim yitein chein*, Hashem makes people like someone who is humble. Because you sewed the suit with humility, Hashem made it look much nicer."

The Rav looked straight at Shimon. "Remember this whenever you sew more suits and you will always be successful."

We don't enjoy being around someone who thinks he's better than everyone else. "Let's be humble, and then we can be sure that people will like us."

Do Your Best

One day, in the small town of Kosava, Lithuania, Avraham Yeshaya Karelitz was looking for his friend. Avraham Yeshaya was always at his *shtender* learning, but today he had a problem. He had borrowed money from his friend Aharon just last week, and he couldn't seem to find him anywhere to pay him back.

"Shmuel, have you seen Aharon Horowitz anywhere?" he asked a friend.

"No," came the reply. "He seems to have disappeared from town."

Avraham Yeshaya would ask people visiting from other towns if they had heard of his friend. Nobody knew who Aharon was.

Years passed. Avraham Yeshaya moved to Bnei Brak, in Eretz Yisrael. Soon, he became known as the great Chazon Ish. All the while, he never stopped searching for his friend, to repay what he owed.

In 1954, the Chazon Ish was *niftar*. News of his passing spread quickly. Announcements were made and posters were hung up everywhere. People all over the world were sad that the *gadol hador* was gone.

Aharon Horowitz lived in Tel-Aviv all that time. He saw one of the many posters and read the name on it.

Avraham Yeshaya Karelitz … he said to himself thoughtfully. *Hmmm … I know that name from somewhere …. Oh, that's right! My friend from Kosava, many years ago! Wow, he became the gadol hador?! Perhaps I should visit his family as an old friend of his ….*

When he walked into the home where the family was sitting *shivah*, the Chazon Ish's brother, R' Meir, noticed him and asked him his name.

"Aharon Horowitz," he replied. "We were friends back in Kosava, many years ago."

"Aharon Horowitz?! *Aharon* Horowitz from Kosava??! My brother, Avraham Yeshaya, has been looking for you for so long! He wanted to repay you for the money you lent to him so many years ago, and now you're here!"

R' Meir jumped up from his chair and ran to get the money to repay what his brother had owed. Hashem made sure the *tzaddik* wouldn't be left with a debt.

The Chazon Ish had done all he could to pay back his loan, but for so many years he was not successful. He tried as hard as he could and then Hashem did the rest.

As long as we try our best to do what Hashem wants from us, we don't have to worry. Hashem sees our effort, and He will take care of whatever we were not able to do.

The Great Juice Story

R abbi Daniel Frisch was a great *mekubal* and *talmid chacham* who lived not too long ago. It was hard for R' Daniel to write because his hand was always getting infected, but he still wrote many *sefarim*. He would often travel to America to raise money to print his *sefarim*.

On one trip, R' Frisch was staying with the Nussbaum family. They felt very honored to have him as their guest. Rabbi Frisch was sitting at the desk in his room until late at night, learning and writing. He worked with a small light, humming and smiling to himself, in spite of the fact that it was painful for him to write.

Moshe was one of the Nussbaum children. He felt especially proud that such a *gadol* was staying with them. *Rabbi Frisch is going to leave tomorrow*, he thought to himself. *I must grab all the time I have to speak with him in learning!*

He headed upstairs to the *gadol's* room and knocked softly on the door. Rabbi Frisch invited him in with a smile. The two of them spoke for quite a while. Moshe was getting ready to leave so the Rav could continue learning and writing. He just wanted to get a peek at what the Rav was writing. He leaned over and —

Splash!

The cup of grape juice that Moshe was carrying spilled, drenching the Rav's precious notes.

Moshe felt terrible. He felt more than terrible. It was no secret that anything Rabbi Frisch wrote came with a lot of pain. Moshe tried to help clean up the papers and dry them, but the damage was already done. The papers were stained and unreadable.

"I'm so sorry, Rabbi!" Moshe cried with tears in his eyes. "Please, forgive me, *please*! Oh, what have I done!"

"Moshe," Rabbi Frisch said in calm voice, "let me explain something to you. Many, many years ago, before either of us was created, Hashem

decided what would happen to each person during their life. He decided that on this very day, at this very hour, there should be this juice spilled on the writings of Daniel Frisch. If this is Hashem's plan, there is nothing for me to be upset about."

Rabbi Frisch teaches us something so powerful, yet so simple. He teaches us the first step in emunah. We all have small things that frustrate us. Perhaps you tripped and fell, or you forgot something you needed at home. Take the first step in believing that it's from Hashem, Who knows what's best for us. You will be happy you did.

Battle Cry

Naava fastened her seatbelt excitedly. In a few more moments they would be landing in Israel! It had been many years since she had visited Eretz Yisrael with her husband, Avi. She closed her eyes and tried to rest.

After landing, Naava and Avi went first to the *Kosel*. Naava felt real tears as she *davened* for her family and for Yerushalayim. Just last summer there had been a war, and Naava wished Eretz Yisrael could just have peace. She then walked back to meet Avi.

"It's almost suppertime, we should find a place to eat," Avi said.

They found a beautiful restaurant. They sat down and a waiter came to take their orders. "Shalom, my name is Barack. What can I bring you today?"

As they waited for their order, Naava said, "I must find out that waiter's mother's name. Last summer I *davened* for a soldier who was fighting in the Gaza war. The name I got was Barack ben Orna. I've been *davening* for him the whole year. Just last week, I looked at the paper with his name on it and wondered if he came home alive and healthy. I *davened* that Hashem should just let me know *somehow* how he is doing."

The waiter returned shortly with their order.

"Tell me," Avi said, "is your mother's name Orna by any chance?"

Barack almost dropped the bowl of soup. "Yes!" he replied. "But why do you ask?"

"And did you fight in Gaza last summer?" Avi continued.

"I did. But how do you know all of this?!"

"My wife has been praying all this time for a soldier named Barack ben Orna to return home safely. I am so happy to see that you are safe and well!"

Barack had tears in his eyes. "What? You mean you were praying for me? Yes … I really did come home safely! Thank you," Barack whispered, his voice getting stuck with his tears.

Avi and Barack exchanged numbers, promising to keep in touch.

About a month later, Avi received a phone call from Barack. Barack said that he felt so touched by Hashem's *hashgachah*. "How likely could it be to meet the very lady who lived in America and was praying for me? Since we've met I decided to learn Torah and become religious; now I put on *tefillin* every day.

When we daven for someone else, we may not see how our tefillos are helping them. But every tefillah is answered. It has the power to accomplish more than we could ever imagine.

Cleaning Help

Chaya was a wonderful girl in every way. She was kind and generous, smiling and warm, sincere and helpful. When the time came for her to search for a husband, everyone was sure she would find one right away.

But that's not what happened. Instead, Chaya got older and older, and it seemed that no man was meant for her. People began to forget about Chaya. She was 28. It looked like nobody cared about her.

Chaya did not give up. She knew there was someone there for her. It was hard to be the only one of her friends not married. But she kept *davening*.

One day, while Chaya was eating lunch in the kitchen, there was a new cleaning lady in her house. Chaya smiled and left the kitchen, so the woman could clean more easily. Later, the cleaning woman was speaking to Chaya's mother.

"… A few blocks down," she was saying, "there's a wonderful boy, 30 years old. They also say he's the best, and he *is* special, very special. Maybe for Chaya?"

Chaya could hardly hold back her laughter. A cleaning lady? With a *shidduch* for her?! Now, *that* was funny.

Nevertheless, Chaya's parents inquired about the boy. Sure enough, Yehuda Weissman was a wonderful *bachur*. Within a few weeks, Chaya and Yehuda were engaged to each other.

At the engagement party, Chaya's father got up to speak.

"For ten years we have been searching for a *chassan*, but nothing ever worked out. A few weeks ago, we heard about this wonderful boy from none other than our new cleaning lady. Not only that, but he has been living around the corner all this time! We must learn from this that Hashem oversees everything. He decides when it is the right time for a person to

find their *shidduch*. All the phone calls in the world won't make it happen sooner. Hashem knows the right person *and* the right time!

"Yeshuas Hashem k'heref ayin." Hashem's help comes as fast as the blink of an eye. We need to believe in Hashem's love, and know that He can always come through for us — many times, in ways we could never have dreamt about.

Friendly Competition

Rena and Aliza stood at the store's freezer for a long time. "I like the cookies-and-cream cone very much," said Aliza, "but I also like ice cream sandwiches and sour ices!"

"Well, I think I'm just going to get the éclair pop," Rena said finally. "I like the cookie crumbs on the outside. Oh, so then maybe I should get the cookies-and-cream cone like you!"

The girls were getting ice cream to help cool themselves off on a hot day, but were having a hard time deciding on a flavor.

"Girls," Mr. Simon called from his register, "how about if I tell you a story? It has to do with the companies that make the ice creams that you're looking at."

Mr. Simon began:

"One hot summer day like today, there was a major blackout. Lights stopped working, and freezers became warm. It was a big crisis for companies that need fridges and freezers. Among these companies were Klein's and Mehadrin. They are the two leading companies that make kosher ice cream. And ice cream, as I'm sure you know, needs a freezer!

"Mehadrin called many people to help get the power turned on. But the earliest they would get their electric back would be in two whole days! They were so sad! What would become of the thousands of dollars of ice cream that would melt?!

"Klein's, however, got their electricity fixed in five hours. The Klein brothers knew the trouble Mehadrin was in. They also knew that Mehadrin is their biggest competitor. Both companies try to sell as much ice cream as they can. But the Klein brothers did not think twice about helping.

"'Bring your trucks of ice cream over to us,' they said. 'Plug your trucks into our electricity and save your products!'

"The managers at Mehadrin were so grateful! Klein's had saved all their ice cream, yogurt, and more! The Kleins did not worry about helping the other company and not having as much business for themselves. They just said, 'Hashem is in charge of the money we make.'

"The Klein brothers truly trust in Hashem. They know that everything they have comes from Hashem. They don't worry about other companies taking their business. This makes a tremendous *Kiddush Hashem*."

The girls looked at the ice cream with respect. Rena picked up a Mehadrin peanut butter éclair while Aliza chose the Klein's cookies-and-cream cone.

They sat down to eat the ice cream, hoping to one day make a *Kiddush Hashem* themselves.

We all have situations that come up where we too can make the right choice and make a Kiddush Hashem!

Calm and Connected

"Attention, all passengers. Flight 404 to Israel is expecting a 4-hour delay. We apologize for any inconvenience this may cause." The announcement rang loud and clear in the airport. The passengers were upset, and they complained.

"*May* cause?!? I'll miss my meeting!"

"Oh no! my sister is getting married tomorrow. How will I make it to the wedding on time?!"

"This is terrible!"

One of the passengers was R' Ezriel Tauber. He heard the announcement and calmly took out a *sefer*. He learned while he waited.

Professor Michael David was from Israel and was also waiting for that flight. He watched how calmly Rabbi Tauber accepted the delay without complaining.

"Rabbi," he said, shaking his hand, "aren't you in a hurry to get to Israel?"

"Why do you ask? I was actually scheduled to speak to a very large crowd. With this 4-hour delay, I will not make it to the event," Rabbi Tauber explained.

"What?" the professor exclaimed. "You mean thousands of people will be waiting to hear you speak but you will not show up? How can you be so calm?!"

"I know that Hashem is in full control. We believe that '*Kol akava l'tovah*,' every delay is for the best. So why should I get upset or be angry? Hashem decided that it's better for me to reach Israel later."

The professor was amazed. Eventually, they arrived in Israel, and they each went their separate ways.

Fifteen years later, Professor David noticed a familiar rabbi next to him in shul.

"Rabbi Tauber! Do you recognize me?"

Rabbi Tauber looked up in surprise. "No, I actually do not. What is your name?"

"I am Professor David from the airport fifteen years ago! When I saw that you were the only one who was calm, I decided that I wanted to be like you. What a nice way to live! I hired a rabbi to teach me, and here I am. I now keep Shabbos, and I learn Torah in the morning and evening. It's all thanks to you."

Rabbi Tauber hugged the professor, who now wore a yarmulke and *tzitzis*. "All these years I was trying to figure out how not giving a speech to so many people was a good thing. Today you gave me the answer. With that delay, I was able to bring a Jew back to Hashem. What could be better?"

Everything that happens to someone has a good reason. If we trust Hashem, we will always be happy, calm, and never upset.

Giving Is Getting

"*Mazel tov!*"

Sounds of joy came from the Browns' home. Their daughter Yehudit had just gotten engaged! The Browns did not have much money. Therefore, Mrs. Brown called up an organization called Yad Eliezer. Yad Eliezer owns two wedding halls in Israel. They rent these halls at a low price to families that need them.

"Which hall do you have available for us?" she asked the volunteer on the other line.

"Actually, they're both available right now. We can give you Tiferes Simchah, which is the bigger hall, or Bais Aviva which is a little smaller."

Mrs. Brown booked the bigger hall.

Somewhere else, another girl became a *kallah*. Chana Fried's mother was in the kitchen, already making phone calls. She too, called Yad Eliezer. But when the volunteer heard the date that they wanted, she was very apologetic. "I'm sorry, but that date was already taken for the bigger hall. I can give you the Bais Aviva hall if you'd like."

Mrs. Fried groaned. "Are you sure? We really need that big hall. We have lots of family coming from America."

The volunteer suggested that she call the Browns and see if they would switch with her. Mrs. Fried called immediately.

Mrs. Brown shook her head. "I'm sorry, but we really need the extra space."

Mrs. Fried swallowed and nodded. "I understand. Okay. Thank you very much."

Mrs. Brown hung up and thought. *Maybe I should give it to her, she wants it so much. No, but we need it! Why do they deserve it more than we do? She shouldn't have even asked me. Now she's making me feel bad about it. But maybe … maybe this mitzvah will be a big zechus for Yehudit and her chassan.* Mrs. Brown called Mrs. Fried back and told her that she can have the bigger hall.

Mrs. Fried was ecstatic. "You would do that for me?" she exclaimed. That made Mrs. Brown feel so good about the mitzvah she was doing.

On the day of the girls' wedding, Yad Eliezer got a call from America. A man wanted to pay for one of the weddings that they were having in their halls. "I want to sponsor the wedding in the smaller hall. If a family is making a wedding in the smaller hall, it must mean they can't afford more."

That night, Yad Eliezer told Mrs. Brown that the whole wedding was paid for! She said, "Thank You, Hashem," and marveled at Hashem's kindness.

There are times that you may be asked to give up something that really belongs to you. You may feel that it isn't fair and you have a right to say no. But Hashem is giving you a big test. You will only gain by giving in.

One in a Hundred

Shneur was both excited and nervous. A great Rebbe was interested in seeing if Shneur would be a good husband for his daughter. Shneur knew that the great Rebbe would be testing him on his learning. He brought his Gemara with him to review while he traveled to the Rebbe.

The wagon driver drove quickly, yet carefully. The roads were bumpy, and sometimes they had to travel through deep puddles. Shneur just kept on learning. Suddenly, there was a jerk, and Shneur bounced in his seat. They'd just gone through a deep hole. Shneur's Gemara flew out of his hands and landed on the road! He jumped up —

"Wait, wait," he cried to the driver. "I just dropped my Gemara!" The driver did not hear Shneur. And so, he just rode on, trampling right over Shneur's precious Gemara.

Shneur watched painfully as his Gemara became all muddy. His shoulders felt very heavy as he realized that he had only one page of the Gemara. That page had ripped out and remained in his hand when the Gemara fell on the road. It was from the middle of the *masechta* that he was learning.

Shneur tried to remind himself — "*Gam zu l'tovah!*" this too is for the best — and he immediately began to study from that one page.

Before long, they arrived at the city where the Rebbe lived. He had a shining face, and a warm, welcoming smile.

"Come sit down," he invited him. "Which *masechta* are you learning?" he asked the young boy.

"*Bava Metzia,*" Shneur replied.

Bava Metzia is a long masechta with 119 dafim, the Rav thought. *I don't want to ask him a question from the beginning. He probably*

reviewed that many times. I will ask him a question from right in the middle.

As Shneur began to answer the Rav's questions, he realized that the Rav was asking him questions about the exact page that he had studied from!

The Rebbe was very impressed with Shneur. A few hours later, it became official. Shneur would become the Rebbe's son-in-law!

Shneur saw the hand of Hashem so clearly. Hashem wanted him to marry the Rebbe's daughter and worked it out so perfectly.

We have all seen this many times. When Hashem chooses whom someone will marry, nothing can stand in the way. We must stay calm and trust in Hashem. After all, He knows best and loves us the most.

With Strings Attached

"Sarah," Rabbi Moshe Pardo told his wife, "I've booked a ticket to America. I must go to collect money for our yeshivah."

One week later, Rabbi Pardo arrived in America. Right away, he began making appointments with people who would help his yeshivah.

Shortly after, Rav Pardo began to feel sick. His head felt heavy and his knees and hands were shaky. He couldn't go collecting while feeling this way. With a frown, he called to cancel his meetings. *Why is this happening to me?!* he thought. *I am here to do a mitzvah! Doesn't the Gemara say that anyone who goes to do a mitzvah will not get hurt?*

Rav Pardo went to see a doctor. As the doctor checked him, he noticed that Rav Pardo was wearing *tzitzis*.

"Wow, Rabbi!" he exclaimed. "Do people still wear those strings on their clothing these days? I remember wearing them when I was a young boy!"

Rabbi Pardo reached into his leather bag and took out a magnificent pair of *tefillin*. He handed it to the doctor, explaining that he had brought a few sets as gifts for the people who were going to help his yeshivah. "I'm ready to give this set to you as a gift, if you will agree to put them on every day." The doctor placed his stethoscope around his neck and held the *tefillin* with care.

"It's a deal, Rabbi. And if I ever make it to Israel, I'll be sure to come and visit the yeshivah you told me about."

The next day, Rabbi Pardo, surprisingly, felt a lot better and began to collect money for his yeshivah. He collected what he needed and went back to Eretz Yisrael

Many years passed. One day, someone came to see him.

It was the doctor. "Rabbi," he said with a big smile, "I haven't missed a single day since you gave me the *tefillin*! And now I am here to see your yeshivah."

Rabbi Pardo led him through the hallways and classrooms. He even took him to the kitchen where the meals were prepared for the students.

The doctor was very impressed. "I don't have any children, but I do have a lot of money that I would like to donate."

Rav Pardo shook the doctor's hand. *I wondered why Hashem was causing me to be sick while doing a mitzvah. Now I see that I was able to bring a Jew back to Hashem, and raise more money than I could ever have imagined!*

> *Whenever something happens to upset us, we must train ourselves to remember that everything Hashem does is for a reason. One day we may see why, but our challenge is to trust in Him now.*

A Selfless Bar Mitzvah

Shaul packed his suitcase excitedly. He lived in Yerushalayim and was going on a trip to America with his father and twin brother, Yoni, for their bar mitzvah. He could hardly wait!

Right after landing, their first stop was to Rabbi Weber, their father's friend. They knocked on his door, but instead of inviting them in, he was in a rush to leave.

"I'm really sorry, R' Baruch," he told their father, "but I must leave right now to save a baby's life. Someone from my shul has waited ten years for children. They had a baby who's now very sick. The doctors say there's little hope, but we must do all we can! There's a treatment that may help, but it costs $20,000. We have $10,000, and I must go now and raise the other $10,000. I'm sorry for this short visit."

Shaul's eyes grew wide. "Abba," he whispered, "can you give him the money?"

His father shook his head. "Shaul, this trip is costing me a lot of money. Plus, we're planning a big bar mitzvah party for you and Yoni when we get back. I can't afford another $10,000."

Shaul looked disappointed. "What if we don't have a party?" Shaul looked at Yoni who was nodding in agreement.

"Are you sure about this?" their father asked unbelievingly. His sons nodded, and he wrote a check for $10,000.

A few weeks later, the twins had a bar mitzvah supper in their grandparents' home instead of a party in a big hall. They were dancing with their siblings when, suddenly, in walked Rabbi Weber.

"I have good news for you," he cried. "The treatment was successful, and they expect the baby to live!" Rabbi Weber came all the way to

Israel to present these boys with a special gift on their bar mitzvah for doing such a great mitzvah.

The boys were so happy and they danced and sang with joy like never before.

Twenty-five years later, Shaul greeted his brother Yoni and family at the bar mitzvah of his son Michoel.

"Remember our bar mitzvah?" Yoni asked with a smile. "That was special."

Out of the corner of his eye, Shaul saw someone familiar.

"Rabbi Weber!" he exclaimed. "What an honor!" He handed the special guest the microphone and asked him to speak.

Instead of taking it, Rabbi Weber handed the microphone to a young man who was standing next to him with a wife and two children.

"Twenty-five years ago," the man told the crowd, "Shaul and Yoni gave up their bar mitzvah party to save a baby's life. I was that baby, and these are my children. They didn't only save me, they saved my children as well. We all came together to thank them."

Once again, the crowd danced and sang with happiness like never before.

We cannot imagine what kind of effect our mitzvos have.
Let's try to make the most of every opportunity.

The Real Boss

"Tell me," Mr. Brooks said, leaning back in his office chair, "does Shlomo come to work on time? Does Eli do his work or talk on the phone?"

Aharon Eiger looked at his boss in surprise. Did Mr. Brooks really expect him to speak *lashon hara* about the friends he worked with? "I'm sorry, Mr. Brooks, but you know that I really can't answer these questions. It would be *lashon hara*."

"Really!" Mr. Brooks exclaimed, getting red with anger. "We'll see how long that lasts."

The next day, Aharon arrived at work to find his office locked. He tried to use his key, but it seemed that someone had changed the lock on his door. After many hours of waiting for a locksmith to come and open the door, Aharon finally got into his office. By then, he had lost a lot of time that he could've been working.

"So! Do you think now is a good time to chat about your friend Shlomo? Or maybe we should speak about Yehuda; maybe he's not such a close friend to you," Aharon heard his boss say at the door.

"I will not speak *lashon hara* about anyone," Aharon said firmly.

The next few months were hard ones for Aharon. Mr. Brooks tried everything he could to make Aharon tell him all the bad things that the workers might be doing. Still, Aharon did not give in.

One day, Mr. Brooks made it very hard for Aharon. Aharon was tired of all the tricks. *Maybe I should just go work somewhere else,* Aharon thought. But suddenly, his office door opened and Mr. Brooks was there with a big smile on his face.

"Aharon," he said, putting his arm around him, "from now on, we are friends. I am going to give you an important job in our company."

Aharon was afraid that this was another way Mr. Brooks was trying to trick him.

"Why are you suddenly acting so kind to me?" he asked.

"I'll need to begin traveling a lot for our business and I won't be in the office. I need someone whom I can trust not to tell people information about the business. You know how to keep your mouth closed no matter what anyone might do to you. You are perfect for this important job; I know I can trust you."

Because Aharon stayed strong, and didn't speak *lashon hara*, Hashem rewarded him with a better job.

Has someone ever asked you to do something that you knew was wrong, yet you were too afraid of them to refuse? What we must really fear, however, is committing a sin. Aharon was only afraid of speaking lashon hara; he was not afraid of his boss. Hashem will reward all of those who stay strong to do His mitzvos.

The Cry of a Baby

Nochum poked his chicken with his fork and sighed. Just today, he and his wife Malky had heard the sad news. The doctor could not help them. Nochum and his wife Malky had been married for almost fifteen years. They still did not have any children.

That's it! he said to himself. *I am tired of always davening for children. It's so disappointing to be let down again and again! This is what Hashem has decreed and I am willing to accept it. Starting tomorrow, I will daven for other things. Maybe to buy that house we really like, or that Malky should get a raise from her boss....*

With that, Nochum finished the chicken and put his plate in the sink.

The next morning, Nochum went to *daven* at his 6 o'clock minyan. He was *davening* with his usual *kavanah* — but today there was just one difference. At the point in his *Shemoneh Esrei* where he'd been *davening* for children for the past fourteen-and-a-half years, Nochum began asking for other things.

Just then, the sound of a newborn crying was heard from the back of the shul. The baby's wails grew louder and louder in the quiet room. Nochum continued to sway back and forth, but he could not get out the words he had planned to say.

"Hashem," his body shook as he cried, "I don't know what a baby is doing in the shul. But I *do* know that this is a sign from You that I should not give up. Father in Heaven, it's been so many heartbreaking, disappointing years. Malky and I are aching for a child. Please, Hashem, don't turn me away this time!"

Less than a year later, Nochum was back at the shul, only this time he was the *avi haben*, father of his newborn son at his *bris*.

Nochum stood up to speak to the guests who had come to the *bris*. With tears, he told the story of how a baby's cries changed everything. When he sat down, a man came to him and explained.

"It was my baby who cried during *davening*. My wife was up all night with the baby. At 5 o'clock in the morning he finally fell asleep. I decided to take him to shul with me to give my wife a chance to sleep. It was during *Shemoneh Esrei* that he woke up and you heard him cry."

Hashem plans everything perfectly. He caused the baby to cry at the exact moment that Nochum used to pray for children.

We see how much love Hashem has for us. He never wants us to stop davening because He knows that is the way we can receive so many presents from Him.

All From Hashem

oshe was jealous of his neighbor, Yosef. Yosef was smart and had lots of friends. One day, Moshe did a very wrong thing. He said lots of bad things about Yosef. People believed him and stayed away from Yosef.

One day, the *shadchan* came. "Yosef!" his mother cried, clapping her hands. "The *shadchan* has a great girl for you — the daughter of the *shochet* from the next town."

But Moshe's rumors had spread very far. The *shochet* heard the bad stories and shook his head. He didn't want his daughter to marry Yosef.

At that time, the Russian Army demanded that all unmarried men join the army. It was not long before Yosef had to join the army. At home, his mother cried. "Yosef could have been married and saved from the army," she wailed to her husband.

Yosef suffered terribly in the army. The Russian soldiers were mean to Jews.

"Roll call!" the general would call. Every man had to run out and be dressed in his heavy uniform. They fought wars in dangerous places. Yosef often went hungry, because he didn't want to eat the non-kosher food.

Eight years passed, and Yosef was finally allowed to leave the army. Moshe was married and still lived in the same town. When he saw Yosef, Moshe immediately felt sorry for what he had done. *But how can I tell him that I said those things about him?! He will tell everyone, and then people will hate me!*

Moshe kept thinking about Yosef. Finally, he made up his mind.

I'll ask the Alter of Slabodka, R' Nosson Tzvi Finkel, to ask Yosef to forgive me.

A few days later, Yosef received a message that R' Nosson Tzvi wanted to speak with him.

The Alter told Yosef about the rumors the boy had spread about him. The Alter looked deeply into Yosef's eyes and held his hand.

"That boy now wants you to forgive him."

"I forgive him, of course," Yosef replied.

"Are you sure, Yosef? How can you forgive him so easily?!"

"I believe that **no one can do anything to me unless Hashem wants it to happen**. And if going to the army and losing a *shidduch* is what Hashem wanted, then I am truly happy. It must have been the best thing for me," Yosef said strongly.

Rav Nosson Tzvi looked at his *talmid* with love. "You are a true *tzaddik*," he said, kissing his forehead. "And you are right."

Let's learn this lesson from Yosef. No one can do anything to us unless Hashem wants it to happen. Hashem loves those who accept everything He does without complaining. This is very hard to do. However, it makes us so great and Hashem will give us a big reward for it.

This Too Is for the Best

Mrs. Oelbaum, principal of Tiferes Ahuva, made a telephone call to Esther. She said, "We would love to have you as our second-grade teacher."

Esther held the phone tightly. She could hardly believe it! She had given a model lesson there last week, and now they wanted her to be a teacher in the school!

"Mommy, I got the job!" she exclaimed happily. She got right to work in preparing everything she needed for the coming school year.

It was now a week before school was to start. Esther already had her teacher's bag packed when she received another phone call from Mrs. Oelbaum.

"Esther, I hate to do this to you, but the job we offered you is no longer available." Esther's mouth felt very dry. "The second grade teacher told us that she *would* be coming back to teach, since her other job didn't work out. I am very, very sorry."

Esther hung up the phone and put her head down on the table. "What should I do now?" she moaned. "I could've gotten ten other jobs if I had known this would happen!"

A few minutes passed and Esther began feeling a little bit better. *Obviously, Hashem didn't want me to know. He wanted me to be doing something else this year.*

Within the next few days, Esther found a job as a secretary in an office near her house. It was not at all what she had wanted, but she accepted it from Hashem.

"Chaya, can you please pass the stapler?" she called to the other girl who worked in the office with her.

"Sure," Chaya responded thoughtfully. *I really like Esther,* she thought. *She's kind, cheerful, and so calm. I think she'd be a perfect shidduch for my older brother, Yossi.*

Within a short time, Esther was a *kallah* and married Yossi. She had really wanted to teach at Tiferes Ahuva, but the office job that Hashem led Esther to ended up getting her the perfect *shidduch*.

At one of their *sheva brachos*, Esther's father stood up to make a speech. He told the crowd this story.

Yes, Esther thought that the teaching job would be best for her. But Hashem always knows what's best. She got so much more than she could have ever hoped for!

Sometimes things may look bad at first and it's not easy to say "Gam zu l'tovah," this is for the good. But as we see from Esther, Hashem knows the place and circumstances that are best for us. When we realize this, it will be so easy to say "Gam zu l'tovah" — we will even say it joyfully!